BAD BLOOD

To Steve Robertson,

Thank you for sharing your artistic talents with us all. You captured the essence of Mayport in your artwork. It was an honor to be your friend. You will be missed.

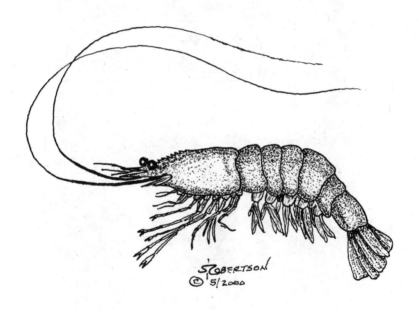

These are true stories. Some names have been changed and at times you will only read first names. It will be much better that way.

THE WORST BUT NOT THE FIRST

The fact that five people were murdered in a trailer on a main street in Mayport, Florida, near Mr. John King's haunted house, brought shock and horror to the family members of the victims and to the general public. However, such horror is not new to Mayport's history. It is only new to the generation that dwells there, now. For the old timers still living in Mayport or the near vicinity, this awful tragedy will be added to the other horrific events of the past. This most recent sadness may go down in Mayport history as the worst, but it is definitely not the first.

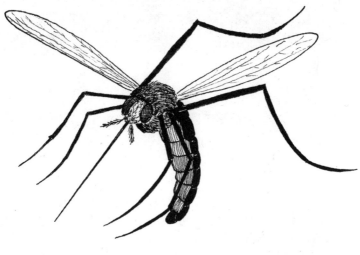

S.C.OBERTSON
© 10/2000

MAYPORT, FLORIDA U.S.A.

Mayport, Florida is a small fishing village located near the Atlantic Ocean at the mouth of the North flowing St. Johns River.

THE MAYPORT MURDERS

I turned to the television when a local newscaster
said the two words, "Mayport Murders". There it was in
big letters on the screen; under the caption was a picture
of a hard looking young man. There are no good police
mug-shots and this one was no exception. In fact a
mug-shot picture can make you look even crazier than
you really are but not in this particular case. I didn't
know the man, but I recognized him because I had seen
him on a number of occasions when I was in the town
of Mayport, Florida. I was, however, familiar with the
name, William Wells. The young man on the television
screen was not the William Wells I knew from my past
and younger days, but I recognized the wild look in his
eyes. The young man was definitely related in some
way to the William Wells I did know.

The newscaster proclaimed, "William 'Billy' Wells
was taken into custody by the Jacksonville Sheriff's
Office S.W.A.T team for the possible murders of five
individuals after a dramatic twelve hour standoff and
hostage situation in Mayport, Florida."

My telephone rang and it was my mother. She recognized the name and she actually knew the young man. "Are you watching the news?"

"Yes ma'am. I don't know this boy."

"He's Billy Wells' half brother. They've got the same daddy, but different mamas and the same name. You remember William Wells don't ya? This boy's name is Billy, too. This is just awful. I feel terrible about this. Go on and watch it. I'll talk to you later."

When I hung up the phone I reached into my shirt pocket and pulled out a small folded piece of paper. I opened it and read the words I had written that morning: *Don't forget to write about the fight with Billy and David at the Mayport schoolhouse.*

Earlier that same day, before I saw the disturbing newscast about the Mayport murders, I was signing copies of my books at a local bookstore. I have written a series of historical novels based on the gothic southern history of the town of Mayport, Florida. I have been criticized from time-to-time for the subject matter of my writings. The members of the older and more established generations of the small fishing village feel I look to the dark side of the town and over look the good moments and honorable citizens who have lived there in the past and at the present. I do know many kind and wonderful individuals and families from my time in Mayport. I write about what I remember and the stories I have been told.

There has been more than one Billy Wells who walked the streets of Mayport. The Billy Wells who killed five people in that trailer had a half brother, also named Billy. They were at least 25 years apart.

When I saw the name, Billy Wells, on the television screen it ignited memories I could not contain. The memory flashes of the Billy Wells I knew in my younger days in Mayport, opened a mental Pandora's Box of fear, pain and evil. The fact I had already been thinking about a Billy Wells' story added to the number of flashes from the past pounding in my head.

Isn't it interesting how we remember the people who scared us during our younger days? Being afraid seems to stay with us longer than other emotions. Intimidation and creating fear in others are characteristics in many people. These folks actually live to scare others. It becomes a way of life, or death, if you will.

Scaring others, especially children, is a trait of the South. It has been said that, "Fear and respect go hand in hand." The history of many southern families has been to scare children into behaving. Or even sometimes it is used in jest with the outcome not so funny for the recipient. It becomes a mean spirited tradition and is carried to an extreme on many occasions. There is no fun in being afraid.

The so called Mayport Murders were committed in a trailer next to Mr. John King's haunted house and directly across the street from the local restaurant known as Bill and Angie's. The restaurant was formally known as Parnell's, Parson's, the Blue Dolphin, Damnifino and then, Bill and Angie's. The building has been leveled now and no longer exists.

The accused killer, Billy Wells, confessed to killing his wife, his wife's brother, her father, his wife's alleged lover and a young black man Billy called a childhood friend and Mayport drug dealer. One of the victims, Billy's father-in-law, was the owner of the restaurant called, Bill and Angie's. His wife Angie died earlier that year. Both families had a history of sadness, tragedies, violence and untimely accidents and deaths.

It is being called the "Mayport Murders" when in reality it is only the next chapter in the dark and violent history surrounding the quiet Florida fishing village at the mouth of the St. Johns River. Mayport Florida, U.S.A. has had decades of unexpected and untimely deaths, tragedies, murders, fatal accidents and as the Georgia blues singer, E. G. Kight would sing, *Evil goin' on.*

The "evil goin' on" in Mayport has been known to have many culprits. Strange and untimely deaths have been a way of life in Mayport forever. Is it because of the drugs and the alcohol? Is it because of the constant frustration of poverty, or perhaps the hopelessness of remaining poor? Could it possibly be the ghosts that walk the floors of Mr. John King's haunted house? Is it the sulfur water, or the stink of the low tide muck? Is there a possibility it could be in the blood; the bad blood?

STOP LOOKING IN THE MUD

Miss Helen May Floyd, a wonderful educator, writer, historian and one of the beloved Mayport citizens, once sent me the lines of a poem saying: *Two prisoners looked from prison bars, one saw the mud, the other saw the stars.* "Stop looking in the mud."

Miss Helen May is no longer with us, but I wish I could tell her I write about the mud, because that is what I remember. I really liked Miss Helen May and her family as I grew up in Mayport. I'm sorry she didn't like my writings. She did write about the early history of Mayport. In Miss Helen May's writings she referred to William Wells Sr. as "Wild Bill". She begins one of her books with this story:

William Wells, also known as "Wild Bill" traded his fishing clothes for a navy uniform early in World War II. Stationed north of the Mason-Dixon Line, he was unhappy with life in a Foreign Land. Naturally, he was soon found to be absent without leave. Before he was picked up by the shore patrol, he was asked why he risked a term in the brig just for a short time at home. "Cuz," he said, "New York is all right, but it's too far from Mayport ever to amount to anything."

When Miss Helen May died, the area in Mayport called the Little Jetties was turned into a fishing park and named in her honor. There is also a memorial plaque near the Mayport Lighthouse quoting more of her writings.

Beneath spreading oaks, partially covered by shifting sands of a long gone hill, there once were rusting wrought iron fences. Tilted headstones covered by blackberry brambles were overshadowed by an oleander tree that was taller than many houses in the village. Here robins flocked in February and violets bloomed in early spring. No one tended the graves and few questioned their origins. This was a place of mystery to the children who sometimes chose it for a playground.

Oak Tree, oleander and tombstones are gone. In the pavement where Broad Street makes a wide semi-circle near the Navy fence are strange indentations. Perhaps they mark the graves of some long gone and long forgotten citizens of Mayport.

Miss Helen May recorded the following events of Mayport tragedies in her historical journal, "In the Shadow of the Lighthouse" (1994). She wrote:

There was a decade of personal tragedies. The Norwegian captain was especially marked. His wife Jessie Viola died in September. His daughter Jessie died in October and his other daughter Laura died in May; all three in the same year.

The death of loved ones during this time in Mayport was followed by a custom that disappeared as land transportation improved. A skipjack bearing the casket would leave Mayport docks and, leading boats loaded with mourners, would thread through nearby creeks to family cemetery plots on Big Talbot Island, New Berlin, or even Dames Point.

During one such sad occasion, a group of mourners saw vultures circling a house on an island in the waterway. They found the dead body of a man in the house. It was a dark discovery for an already sad and dismal day.

An epidemic of Spanish flu affected Mayport's population. Miss Mildred Cason was the first victim. She left five small children behind. As a boatman watched the water-borne funeral move toward New Berlin he said, "This is the saddest sight I've ever seen."

Mayport lost Angelina Singleton, who left several children behind. Fred Tillotson also died. The Tillotston and Singleton children were all transported to the Thornwell Orphanage in South Carolina.

During this decade of tragedy, fire destroyed Fannie Gavagan's store, her residence and one of her rental cottages. Other losses to fire were: A. J. Floyd's hotel, bar, and residence, Dr. Neil Alford's office and drug store, J. D. McCormick's store, post office, and restaurant. A total of fourteen buildings were lost to fires including hotels and other homes.

I was fortunate enough to witness an interesting and strange Mayport moment at a funeral for another Miss Helen. It was a closed casket ceremony at the Mayport cemetery. Pictures of a young and beautiful Miss Helen were placed on the top of the closed casket. It was a calm sunny day as a beautiful young, tall, blonde Mayport woman, Melissa, began to sing the hymn version of the "Lord's Prayer" in honor of Miss Helen. As the young woman's voice moved over the family members and friends, the wind started to blow and the temperature dropped at least twenty degrees in a matter of seconds. Melissa continued singing as the wind blew hard enough to knock the pictures of Miss Helen off the top of the casket. I was standing next to my mother during this strange change in the weather. I have stood with my mother at many Mayport funerals. If someone dies we go to honor them. As the wind picked up, lady's hats were blown off their heads and some people even ran to their cars. I turned to see if my mother was safe and if she wanted to find shelter in my car. I could not believe my eyes.

Large chunks of Spanish moss were being carried by the wind and were wrapping around my mother's body. It was not just a few pieces of the moss. Her legs were wrapped and surrounded first. The soft plant seemed to be working its way up her body. My mother was struggling to free herself from the moss. It was obvious she was in distress, but she was trying to be calm. I stepped to help her, but Mr. Walter, a friend and Mayport citizen got to her first and began pulling at the moss, trying to free her. I joined Mr. Walter and we were able to get the moss off my mother. The wind stopped blowing. I turned to my mother and asked her, "Mama, what just happened here?"

She smiled and in her usual calm voice she said, "That was just Miss Helen's way of sayin' good-bye."

It was the perfect answer; the perfect southern answer. Mayport, Florida has a history of strange events, strange superstitions and strange characters.

The Florida Times-Union newspaper headlines read: *Police think five killed over eleven day period.* Steve Patterson, a Times-Union staff writer, reported that William "Billy" Wells, a twenty-seven year old man, had killed five people and left their bodies in his trailer for 11 days.

IRENE
THE FIRST VICTIM OF THE MAYPORT MURDERS

"It started as an accident", was Billy Wells' initial comment about the first killing. He told the authorities he shot his wife, Irene, as they sat together in their kitchen. His son and stepdaughter were in other rooms of the trailer. Billy said he did not mean to kill his wife. He was joking when he put the gun to her head. He did not think it was loaded.

"I loved her with all my heart. I would have never killed the mother of my children. I would have taken my own life first."

When I read those comments it made me think, *What kind of person points a gun at the back of his wife's head, just playing around?*

Billy said the couple had been having problems and were trying to reconcile. He was massaging Irene's neck when she reached out to the counter and grabbed the pistol and held it in her hand. The idea of a gun sitting out on the kitchen counter with children in the house seems like a strange way to live.

Irene said, "This is in case you get stupid today." Billy did not see any bullets in the gun. He took it from Irene and tossed it into the air. When Irene asked, "What are you going to do, now?" Billy aimed the gun at her head and squeezed the trigger. There was a bullet in the chamber and Irene was shot in the back of the head.

"She gasped for a breath of air and fell over. It looked like I executed her and I knew it as soon as it happened. I lay on the floor for hours in a pool of blood, holding her."

Billy's son and stepdaughter were playing on the computer in another part of the trailer and did not pay any attention to the noise in the kitchen. When he realized they did not know what happened, Billy took his stepdaughter to stay with her grandmother. Billy kept his son with him. The other deaths took place during the next week.

AN INTRODUCTION TO MAYPORT VIOLENCE

I was five years old when I was first introduced to Mayport violence. It was mean, crude, abrupt and everlasting. You remember things that scare you, or at least I do. I'm sure up to that moment, in my young life, I had never seen very much blood, or even thought about blood, for that matter. I had been scared before, because I was surrounded by southern adults, but not with blood added to the mixture. It was the moment when my little brain was jarred into having future memories of what people are calling the dark side. It was not my choice. I was one of those *victims of circumstances; an innocent by-stander.* I would understand and know more, as I grew older, as to the reasons for that first explosion of hate and blood.

My father, George, was definitely in the wrong place. He was a "damn Yankee" from New Bedford, Massachusetts. What on earth was he doing in Bill's Hideaway, the ultimate southern honky tonk? It was located near the big jetty rocks where the St. Johns River meets the Atlantic Ocean on Seminole Beach. The restaurant and dance hall had been built high on wooden pylon stilts so the high tide would not touch the building. George had no business being there. At least that's what the good old Mayport boys thought and made quite clear.

George had joined the United States Navy as an escape from the possibility of grave bodily harm in his hometown. He had thrown a snowball that was packed too tightly. It hit a young girl in the mouth and knocked out her front teeth. Her brother was home on leave from the United States Marine Corps. When he saw his sister he went hunting for the careless snow-baller. At age sixteen George joined the Navy and left his home and relatives in New Bedford. He never went back.

I remember standing next to our car with my mother. I could see my father walking down the wooden steps from Bill's Hideaway. A huge man was following him. There was a crowd of men and women following the big man down the steps. It was the first time I heard the two words, "damn Yankee". The huge man was yelling at my father.

"You better get your damn Yankee ass out of here. We don't want your kind here."

My father got to the bottom of the steps and walked to where I was standing. I thought we were leaving. I thought wrong. The crowd of men and women were now standing at the foot of the steps. The huge man had more to say to my father.

"You better run, boy. I don't want to see you in here again as long as you breathe."

Then the real memories were created for me. My father picked me up and sat me on the hood of our car. He took the watch off of his wrist and handed it to me. "Hold this for your daddy. And watch what I have to do. Don't look away. You need to see what a man has to do sometime."

My mother was in tears. "Come on, George, let's just leave. Please, don't go back over there."

"I have to go back. You know I can't just leave." He looked at me. "Keep watchin' your daddy, boy."

My eyes were glued on him as he walked away. The people who had followed my father and the big man down the steps had formed a big circle and the huge man was standing in the middle, calling for my father to come to him. In my eyes, he was a monster of a man and actually made three of George. I watched my father walk to the middle of the circle and join the big man. I heard a man's voice from the human circle yell, "Kill 'im, Bucky. Send his skinny ass back up North."

The big man was Bucky Thomas. He was the meanest and toughest man in Mayport at that particular time. There would be many more to come, but Bucky Thomas was the "king of the hill" in June of 1954. He was well known and feared for his ability to overpower any man who stood against him. He liked to fight and he had not been beaten. My heart began to pound in my little chest when I saw my father hit the huge man in the face. The crowd exploded with noises of all kinds. Men cheered, women screamed and voices were raised in anger, and even joy, as the fight began.

Later, in my life, I would compare George to a Spanish matador fighting a huge raging bull. Bucky would charge at George with grunts and growls like a wild animal. George would step to the side and throw his fists in flurries of punches. Every time George hit Bucky it was three, four, five punches at a time. Blood splattered each time George's clinched fist hit the big man's face. Bucky remained on his feet after taking the savage beating to his head. His two hundred fifty pound body was no match for George's one hundred sixty pound body of speed and agility. Sometime and somewhere George had been taught to defend himself and he was most confident in what he could do. It was most obvious to me and all watching that this was not his first fight either.

Then it happened, causing the crowd to explode with the loudest noises of all. A fast and strategically placed right fist hit Bucky on his right temple knocking him down flat on his back onto the white beach sand. All of the air exploded out of Bucky's lungs. The huge man rolled over onto his stomach fighting for air and grimacing in pain.

The crowd was somewhat quiet as Bucky struggled in the sand. A few men's voices yelled for him to "get up", but that was easier said than done. I didn't realize until later in my life that my father waited for Bucky to get up before he continued his vicious attack. He did not hit or kick Bucky when he was on the ground. It was honorable, but I did not know that at the time. I often wondered if Bucky would have done the same if George had been lying in the sand at his feet. When Bucky finally got to his feet my father's attack continued. Bucky took a barrage of punches before he fell, face-down in the white sand for the second time. Everyone, even a five-year-old, knew Bucky Thomas was not getting up again.

The crowd was silent in shock. The *King of the Mayport Hill* had been dethroned. Two men went to Bucky's aid, but the huge man was unconscious and dead weight in the soft white beach sand. Physical fatigue, combined with the number of blows to his head had rendered Bucky incapacitated. The two men did turn Bucky over so his face would not be in the sand and to see if he was alive. Bucky grunted and pushed them away as they attempted to assist him.

Then my introduction to violence continued. My father tried to walk out of the human circle, a circle with no southern hospitality. As he turned toward our car a man jumped from the crowd holding a black handle machete above his head in the attack position. George stepped back in his defensive stance as the crowd made one gasping noise of shock, surprise and some delight. When the man stepped to my father, a young teenager ran from the crowd and stood between George and the machete man.

"Don't you cut my Uncle George. It was a fair fight. It ain't right to cut 'im."

A voice came from the crowd. "That's Joe Andreu's boy. Don't cut that boy. Don't you dare cut, Tommy. Let 'em go."

The machete man lowered the huge blade and stepped away from George. My father and Tommy walked out of the circle and came to where my mother and I were standing next to our car. Tommy was sixteen years old. He was my mother's first cousin. His father, Joe Andreu, was my mother's uncle and the man who raised my mother and her brother, Bobby, after their parents died. Joe Andreu's sister was my grandmother, Margarette. She died when my mother was five years old. Tommy was a brave young man and had saved my father from the machete man.

I don't remember all of us getting into the car and leaving. I do remember standing in the back seat of the car and looking out the back window as we drove away. I could see Bucky Thomas running after the car. He staggered and fell in the soft beach sand. He yelled "damn yankee" and a number of other names. He threw shells and rocks at our car as we left him crawling on the beach.

My mother was driving. Tommy was in the back seat with me. George was sitting up front in the passenger seat. His face was covered with blood. He was fatigued and didn't say a word during the ride home. We lived with Uncle Joe, Tommy's father, in a house near the entrance to the United States Naval Base. They called it the Big House.

It was a two-story house with a large lower porch covered by a porch balcony above. Wide round columns supported the upper porch. You could see the Big House had a stately appearance at one time but the weather, and poor upkeep had taken away the glory from the past. It was located directly across the road from the Fish Bowl Restaurant, bar and dance hall. My mother worked at the Fish Bowl as a waitress. She met my father there. She was sixteen years old.

I don't recall much about the ride home, but my next memory is of my father standing on the back porch of the Big House with Uncle Joe pumping a big lip water pump so George could wash the blood off of his face and arms. All of the blood washed off my father. None of the blood was his. It all belonged to Bucky Thomas.

My introduction to the violent side of Mayport was complete. I would see much more violence and be scared many more times as a young boy growing up in Mayport, Florida U.S.A.

One day as an adult, I went to Mayport to meet a few friends at a place called Monty's Marina. When I entered the front of the building an eighty year old Bucky Thomas was sitting at one of the tables. He saw me and announced how much he hated my father. He also said he could not stay in the room with me because I looked too much like George. Bucky Thomas was still missing some front teeth from that awful fight and it was obvious he had never forgotten his first real "ass-whippin'". I did not want to be the cause of Mr. Thomas having some awful flashbacks so I did leave.

MONTY'S MARINA

Recently, I was sitting in Bob's Barber Shop in Atlantic Beach, Florida waiting my turn for a haircut. A huge man walked into the shop. He had an escort and I realized the man was blind when he sat down next to me. I knew the man's face even thought it had aged greatly since the last time I saw it. His name was Red and he had been a Mayport shrimper and citizen all his life. One time he sold a shrimp boat to my father. Bob, the barber, spoke up and said, "Mornin' Red. Guest who's sittin' next to you?"

Red turned in my direction and reached out his hand, touching my leg. "I can't see no more. Who are ya?"

When I told him my name and my father's name, Red's face lit up like a candle. It was obvious that memories were flashing in his head.

"Any time I hear ya daddy's name I think about that fight he had with Bucky Thomas on the beach." The barbershop went silent when Red made his comment about the past. He continued. "It was the changing of the guard in Mayport. That Bucky was a tough mean man. One time I had tied my boat up next to his boat and went home to get some sleep. I woke up with Bucky standing over me on my bed with his legs on each side of my body and a doubled barreled shotgun pointed at my head. I just knew I was gonna die right there in that bed. Bucky said, 'Next time you tie your boat up next to mine, I'll blow your head off. Now, go move your boat.'" The barbershop remained silent as Red remembered. "I got out of that bed and he followed me all the way to the boat, holding that big gun on me all the way. I moved my boat and tried not to talk to or cross Bucky's path again."

MAYPORT ROAD

One night I was riding in the back seat of our car. I'm not sure how old I was at the time, maybe five or six. My father was driving and my mother was sitting on the passenger's side of the car. I do know we were making the turn on Mayport Road that leads to the town of Mayport. The car ran over a bump or something in the road. The car continued to roll for a few seconds when I heard my mother's voice talking to my father.

"George, you just hit something. I think it was a person." I felt the car slowing down as my father took his foot off the gas pedal.

"You think I ran over somebody?"

"It looked like somebody layin' in the road. It was on my side so you couldn't see it."

My father stopped the car and began backing it up to see what he had run over. It turned out to be a black man who had been killed. He had a railroad spike stuck in the back of his neck. Someone had placed his dead body on the side of the road with his head on the road and his body in the sand. Who ever placed him there knew a car would eventually hit his head with a tire and he would be discovered, another violent moment in Mayport history.

COULD HAVE BEEN A DREAM

I was told to go to bed one night when a group of men entered our house with my father. I think I was about seven-years-old. I knew something was wrong. I remember covering myself with a blanket hoping not to hear something I didn't want to hear. I did not remove the blanket even when sweat ran down my chest. I could hear the men's voices. They were loud and all talking at the same time. I could hear my father's voice above the others every now and then, I guess mainly because his was recognizable to me. The men were talking about a black man being burned in the woods near John King's haunted house. They were planning and discussing what they were all going to say when the police came to Mayport. I fell asleep in a bed wet from my sweat and never heard about that night again. For years I called it a dream, but I never have been sure about that.

One of the members of my father's boat crew carried a picture of a dead Honduran native who had been hung by his neck from the mast of the boat while they were shrimping off the coast of Honduras. The man was supposedly caught stealing shrimp off the boat so he was hung as a thief.

ROAD TO THE BIG HOUSE

LET'S SCARE 'EM TO DEATH

When considering the fact that southern adults made a conscious effort to scare children into being good, we must realize how some people became addicted to this ridicules art of fear and intimidation as measures of discipline. It actual became a way of life for some mentally disturbed individuals. It also came from the fact that children were considered second class citizens with no thoughts of their own or say-so what so ever.

Aunt Lily was one of the most notorious culprit of the *let's scare 'em as much as we can* philosophy.

Another interesting trait of Aunt Lily was that a strange odor filled the air whenever she entered a room. She smelled like Vick Salve. She would always hug you when you got close to her and the fumes from the mentholated salve would clear your head up instantly. I often wondered, as I'm sure others did too, where the salve was applied to her body. Was it on her chest in a poultice, or under her arms, or perhaps a more erotic location? No matter where it was located, it was her calling card, it was potent and rather nauseating and you knew when she was approaching.

My great grandmother died in her home known as the Big House. The Big House was located in East Mayport next to the main entrance to the Mayport Naval Base. The United States Navy would eventually take the Big House away from our family, as well as all of East Mayport, to expand the size of the Naval Base.

We called her Gramma Aggie. She was the matriarch and leader of the family. She died while asleep in her bed in an up stairs bedroom of the Big House. They took her body down to the living room area in front of a huge fireplace. The family began to gather for her funeral service within hours of her death. Most of the relatives from far away would stay at the Big House. Another southern incident of not caring or thinking about the children was on the horizon and Aunt Lily would be the ring leader.

Adequate space and bedrooms at the Big House became limited as the relatives began to gather. At the end of the day sleeping arrangements were being discussed. It just so happened that my cousin Richard and I were assigned to sleep in the same bedroom where Gramma Aggie had died earlier that same day. I was six years old and Richard was eight. I couldn't believe what was happening to us. It was very little consolation but, thank God, they did change the bedclothes of that deathbed.

As Richard and I stood next to the bed we had no idea Aunt Lily would be the last person we would see before we climbed into that tainted bed. We both knew any protest of our placement would be met with a harsh response. It was only right for Richard to go first. He was the oldest. My heart raced in my chest as he climbed slowly into the bed and a recognizable odor touched my nose. I did not want to turn to the door. I knew who was standing behind me. Aunt Lily's voice cracked like it was coming from deep down in the swamp. She spoke slowly with a raspy *Swamp Witch Hattie* texture in her voice. There was no doubt she wanted to scare us and she was successful.

"You boys…gonna…be…all…right…in…here?"

She spoke slowly in a strange deep voice, drawing out each word. She was bathing in the glory of another frightful moment for two innocent children. I knew her words of concern had no substance at all.

I turned to see Aunt Lily's smiling face. It was not a good smile. Children know the differences in smiles. I jumped into the bed next to Richard. I guess I felt safer in the deathbed with him than standing with Aunt Lily. She stepped closer to the bed.

"Now, you boys need to stay in this room tonight. There's a lot of grievin' here and adult talk y'all don't need to be hearin'. Y'all don't need to be playin' and laughin' up here and y'all don't need to be roamin' 'round the house. Y'all understand?"

Her eyes were wide open. We both nodded our heads. She turned and walked to the bedroom door. We were already scared enough and I actually thought she had said all she wanted to say, but I was very wrong about that. Aunt Lily lived for such moments and could not let that opportunity get away from her. She stopped at the door and turned to show us her evil smile one more time. Then her words made both our hearts scream. I heard Richard's and I'm sure he heard mine.

"Remember boys, if you get out of that bed tonight, Gramma Aggie will be under it and grab your ankles when your feet hit the floor."

Aunt Lily left us with that frightening and incredible thought. Needless to say, sleep did not come at all. We did not talk and we did not even consider getting out of that bed. We both may have dosed off in the early morning hours, but I don't remember if we did or not. I remember being miserable, tired and ignored the next day.

I have no memories of the days that followed that awful night. I'm sure there is a psychological reason behind my lack of recollection. But I do remember what happened three days later.

I was standing in a funeral line with some relatives. The line ahead of me was moving slowly past Gramma Aggie's body. She was lying in a coffin and each relative and friend was paying their last respects to her. I was surprised when I realized each one of the relatives was kissing Gramma Aggie on her forehead, cheeks and even some were kissing her on her lips. Now, at six-years-old, I had no intention of kissing a dead person, Gramma Aggie or not. I don't really recall kissing her very much when she was alive, so I knew it was not going to happen now that she was dead.

I looked around and realized I was standing with a group of adults and most of the other children were standing together at the back of the line. I had no idea how I got into that adult section of the funeral line.

For some reason I thought my mother was standing next to me. But, that was not true. My stomach went sour when I looked up and saw that I was standing with Aunt Lily on my right and her sister, Aunt Sue on my left. Aunt Sue did not have the unsettling nature that her sister possessed. I stepped closer to Aunt Sue as the line continued to move slowly. I looked around for my mother, but could not see her. Fear ran through my body and I felt the blood flow change directions in my veins. Where was my salvation? Where was my mother? Was there anyone thinking about me at that moment? My head was on a swivel as I moved closer to Gramma Aggie's dead body.

As I stood only two people away, her head looked huge. It was all I could see and it was massive to my eyes. There seemed to be more room on her forehead than I remembered, her nose seemed more spread out over her face and her lips looked to be actually puckered up ready for the good-bye kisses.

Aunt Sue stepped up to Gramma Aggie's huge head and bent over to kiss her on her cheek. She patted Gramma Aggie's hand and moved away. Aunt Lily pushed me with her hip so I would move directly over Gramma Aggie's head. I turned my little head away from Gramma Aggie big head and my nose was an inch away from Aunt Lily's crotch. The smell of Vick Salve filled my nose and actually took my breath away. For a moment I thought I had solved the mystery and I knew where the poultice was located.

As I moved on past Gramma Aggie's dead body, trying not to make any physical contact, an awful moment in Mayport's tragic history and my short life occurred.

I felt a hand cup the back of my neck. I knew instantly the hand belonged to Aunt Lily and it had evil intentions. Now, at six-years-old, I was not going to kiss a dead person anywhere. The pressure from Aunt Lily's hand moved my head forward and I found my lips within striking distance of Gramma Aggie's huge head. I stiffened my neck, trying to stop the forward motion created by Aunt Lily's grip of death. Even a six-year-old can possess super human strength when being scared to death. I resisted, but found out in a split second that Aunt Lily had even more super human strength than a scared six-year-old. She was winning the tug-a-war battle with my skinny little chicken neck. I had only one way out. I let my body go limp and dropped to my knees. This childish, but successful, maneuver caused the needed result for me to break free from the terrible situation. A short struggle with Aunt Lily ensued before my mother came to my rescue.

The disrespectful actions and the confusion I caused were a necessary means of survival that day. The beating I got for causing such a disturbance was well worth it. I would face Aunt Lily many more times as my young life continued. It was always obvious to me she never forgot that day in the funeral line. When Aunt Lily died I did walk past her coffin with the rest of the family. I did not kiss her but I did give her a little smile.

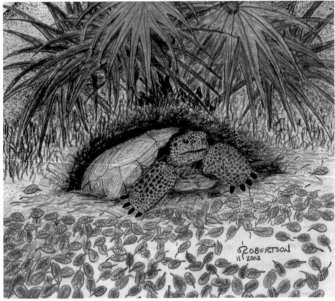

FLORIDA GOPHER TORTOISE

JOHN
THE SECOND VICTIM OF THE MAYPORT MURDERS

After Billy Wells shot his wife, Irene, her brother John, arrived at the trailer looking for her. She was supposed to be working at the restaurant. Billy told the reporter, "John flew into a rage when he saw his sister's dead body on the kitchen floor. He ran to grab the gun on the counter." Billy got to the gun first and shot John, but only wounded him with the first shot. He then fired two more bullets into John's head. John was 32 years old.

HORSE SHOE CUT

For some reason I was standing in front of the big juke box in Silver's Tavern and Package Store at the end of Mayport Road. I had a quarter in my eight-year-old hand. I was looking for a Johnny Ray song my father wanted to hear. I had searched for such songs on a number of occasions. Even to this day I like to play a juke box. I looked back to where my father was sitting at the bar and saw him swing his fist at another man standing near him.

The violent connection of clinched knuckles and facial tissue was loud and strange. The man fell to the wooden floor and did not move at all. My heart raced as my father stood over the man and looked up at me. My heart shuttered even more when he motioned for me to come to him. I don't remember making my legs move but I found myself standing directly over my father's fallen victim. It was almost all my little heart could take when my father stooped down and lifted the unconscious man's head up off of the wooden floor by his hair. There was an awful circular gash around the man's right eye with blood streaming down the side of his face. I think I could have put all four of my fingers into the cut. I did not realize I was getting one of my father's life lessons of being a man.

"Now ya see, son. This is a horse shoe cut." He traced the horseshoe shaped cut with his finger. "When you hit a man right in this area above the eye it usually causes a cut like this and it ends the argument. When a man is incapacitated he can't fight or talk." He dropped the man's head back down to the floor and we left. I never forgot what "incapacitated" meant.

Robertson
5/06

MAYPORT SCHOOL HOUSE

I WANT TO HIT THAT HARD

As an eleven-year-old Mayport boy, my friends were as tough as young boys could be, probably tougher and meaner than your normal group of boys. I knew the strong and handsome Billy Wells because I had seen him in the streets of Mayport and on the docks at the river. He lived near us and directly across from John King's haunted house. His physical prowess and rough attitude were the subject matter of many conversations of the younger citizens of Mayport. Billy was in his late teens so our age difference would enable me to stay at a safe distance from his wrath. With the age difference we had nothing in common, but I would end up being an outside observer of his wild actions. It was unintentional but I seemed to cross his path more than I wanted.

I was attending a recreational summer school at the Mayport Elementary School where the under privileged Mayport children would have meaningful activities for the summer months. It was similar to the Boys and Girls Clubs throughout the city today.

Painting classes, arts and crafts, ping-pong, tumbling, and board games were just a few of the activities available. Each week or so, we would be taken on a trip to swim in the huge swimming pool on the local naval base as one of our activities. A man named John Joca was in charge of the summer school program for the Mayport children. He was one of those great men with the welfare of each child foremost in his heart. He taught the boys tumbling and when they could do front and back flips he taught the boys to dive and do flips off the diving board at the pool. The rough and tumble Mayport boys loved every moment of Mr. Joca's attention and teachings.

I was standing next to the big red Coca-Cola machine in the small lobby at the entrance of the school. There was no thought in my young mind of the event and lesson coming my way. I watched a young man named David put his money into the coin slot of the big red machine. When the noise of the falling coin ended, he pulled the silver-gray hand lever down to release the bottle of Coca-Cola from the hole where it was held. I liked David, because I had seen him talking to the older girls and I thought he was pretty smooth. As David reached for the bottle, I saw Billy Wells walking toward him. My heart began to pound at the sight of him. David was too interested in his drink and did not see Billy approaching. It was easy for me to see, by the angry look on Billy's face, that he had bad intentions and something awful was going to happen to David. I did not want to be there, but it was far too late. There was no other choice for me. I was getting ready to be an unsuspecting and unwilling witness to more Mayport violence.

Things did not move in slow motion like in the movies. On the contrary, it was fast and vicious. As David turned away from the machine holding his bottle, Billy hit him in the face with a lightening fast and crushing clinched fist. David went down and actually slid across the heavily waxed wooden floor until the wall stopped the movement of his body. I have no idea where the bottle of coke went. In my short time of the Earth, I had never seen anyone hit someone so hard and so fast. I also had never seen someone get hit so hard and so fast. I felt like I was in a dream. It was unnatural.

I had seen my father fight with other men, but this was different. This violent moment was close up and I felt like I was part of the action. They were young men closer to my age and I felt that I was much more than a spectator. Of course, that was just in my mind. I knew two things at that moment: I wanted to be able to hit someone that fast and that hard, and I never wanted to be the one who got hit that fast and that hard.

It wasn't actually a fight, because I'm positive there were no other punches, just that one incapacitating blow. I was the witness to my first "sucker punch", that awful crushing blow to an unsuspecting victim. A sucker punch is actually the action of a coward, but I would not realize that until I grew older.

David's mouth was bleeding and I was sure he had no idea what just happened. He wasn't unconscious, but his eyes were glazed over and he had a distant look on his face. I waited to see what Billy would do next. Actually, once again, I had no choice. My feet were frozen to the floor with fear. I was surprised when Billy did not continue his attack. I wanted to see more, since I was frozen to the floor anyway and it would be at David's expense. I guess Billy had done what he came to do.

There was movement to my right as Larry, David's cousin, walked into the small foyer and saw David on the floor against the wall. Larry was in his early twenties and bigger than Billy and David. I didn't think Billy was going to punish David any more, but Larry evidently thought he was.

"Leave him alone, Billy. He's had enough."

I was surprised again, when Billy did not reply at all. He just walked out of the front door and jumped off to the side of the top step down to the grass. When Billy jumped he disappeared from my view, but I knew right away something awful had happened when he reached the ground. There was a blood-curdling scream of pain and I heard Billy cursing with every profane and nasty word he had accumulated in his limited vocabulary. Larry heard the painful scream, too and looked toward the door but he attended to his cousin's needs.

My morbid curiosity moved my feet from their frozen position. I have no idea why, but I stepped slowly to the front door. My heart raced in my chest when I saw Billy crawling on his belly to the bottom step. He was holding his foot and still cursing and writhing in pain. I watched the tough and mean young man grovel on the ground.

I looked down to see that when Billy landed on the ground he had cut his foot. It was not just a little cut. It was an awful gash the length of the bottom of his foot. His foot was sliced open from the base of his big toe to his heel. I had never seen such a cut, but I did not look away. It was another first for me. I looked to the side of the steps and saw what had caused the terrible injury. When Billy jumped off the top step he had landed on a sharp pipe that was sticking up out of the ground. I turned my attention back to Billy as he continued to grimace in pain.

In a matter of seconds, Larry and David joined me at the top of the steps. The three of us stood there looking at Billy. I was sure David was enjoying Billy's painful situation. I'm sure Billy hated being in that vulnerable position with Larry and David watching him from above. My heart started pounding when Billy looked up and with clinched teeth he directed his request to me.

"Go get me some help before I bleed to death."

I looked at Larry. He nodded his head. "Go tell Mr. Joca."

I did not want to leave. I wanted to see what was going to happen next. Larry could see my hesitation. "Go on, now boy. Get Mr. Joca."

I did what Larry said. Larry was training me to be an alter boy for the St. Johns Catholic Church. I liked and respected him. He was very talented with the guitar and his ability to sing and play.

I know training to be an alter boy did not fit with the desire to hit someone as hard as Billy Wells did. My life in Mayport would have many contradictions for a young boy to handle.

When Mr. Joca returned with me, a crowd of children had gathered at the door where Billy was still holding his foot, trying to stop the bleeding. Larry and David had not attempted to help Billy, but it was obvious and understood that he did not expect or want their assistance. Mr. Joca opened a small black bag and took out a bottle of clear alcohol. He stooped down next to Billy and poured the clear liquid directly onto the gash on the bottom of Billy's foot; another first for me. What a great day. I had never seen anyone do that before.

Billy grimaced in more pain as the alcohol cleaned the opened wound. You could tell he wanted to holler in pain, but the crowd of spectators held his screams inside. I knew he deserved the pain he was suffering. I was so glad it was him and not me. I hoped I would be as brave if a cut on my body was ever drenched and cleaned with alcohol. I was scared of Billy Wells, but there was something about him that made me want to be around him even more. I was actually torn between being a member of the many Mayport thugs or one of the three Mayport altar boys. That was some interesting dilemma.

ONCE THEY TURN ON YA

I think I was still eleven when I witnessed another act of Mayport violence. I was hunting one night with my Uncle Joe. He raised my mother after her parents died. Uncle Joe was my grandmother's brother. I don't remember why or how I was out there with Uncle Joe, but I always seemed to be in places I didn't want to be. I really hated hunting, but I didn't want to be a "sissy boy" in the eyes of the family hunters.

I guess it is understood that you must have a dog named Blue if you are a real hunter. Uncle Joe had his Blue with us that night when the prey of the hunt was the opossum, one of the night creatures we would blind with the beam of a flashlight and then blow his nasty butt right out of that tree he considered a safe place to be.

We were only walking a few minutes when Uncle Joe handed me the flashlight and motioned for me to shine it up into a tree directly over our heads. With only a few searching movements of the light the bright beam showed clear on the eyes of our first victim of the night.

Uncle Joe raised his shotgun and blasted that dangerous animal right out of the safety of that big oak tree. Mr. Opossum was dead before he hit the ground. I'm not sure why we were hunting this creature. I don't remember ever eating one. The men of the family talked of days when that was all they had to eat, but they said that about squirrels, robins, gophers and rabbits, too. I really think it was supposed to be for fun and to hone our hunting skills in case we needed survival skills later down the line.

When the dead animal hit the ground Blue ran over and stood next to our dead and bloody victim. Blue only stood there. Uncle Joe walked next to the dog, poked the opossum with the end of the gun barrel, to be sure the animal was dead and would not bite him. Confident that the prey was dead, Uncle Joe reached down to pick the carcass up. As Uncle Joe's hand touched the tail of the opossum Blue made a growling sound, as if he did not want his master to retrieve the bounty. In the brink of an eye, Uncle Joe shot Blue in the head with his shot gun. At such a close range Blue's face seemed to explode as the metal pellets slammed into his head. An almost headless Blue, Uncle Joe's favorite dog, lay dead next to that nasty opossum.

My heart felt like it was exploding in my chest like Blue's head. I thought I would soon wake up from that horrible and ridiculous dream. I think I just stared at the two dead animals, hoping I did not upset Uncle Joe while he was in his killing mood. Then I heard words come from where Uncle Joe stood near the oak tree. I guess it was another lesson to make me a better man and to be able to react properly if I was ever faced with a similar situation. Uncle Joe's voice seemed like he was a teacher with an important philosophy to share for generations to come and I was to carry it with me to give it to another.

"Once they turn on ya, boy, there ain't nothin' left to do, but put 'em down."

JOE JUMPER

I DON'T TELL ON NOBODY

On my second memorable encounter with Billy Wells, a beautiful Mayport girl named Harriett stole my heart. It was the first time a girl caused my heart to race in my chest. Before that only fear made my heart pound. The combination of the physical attraction and the violence seemed to fit the order of each day. Harriett was no doubt one of the most beautiful girls in Mayport at that particular time. She even rivaled the five Canova sisters, but they are definitely a different story.

Harriett was fifteen years old, but looked like she was in her twenties. She was mentally and physically mature far beyond her years. She had long black hair, dark skin from her Portuguese heritage, a perfect round face and she had what was called a "brick house" body. Harriett was not dainty by any stretch of the imagination. If anything, she had a muscular and powerful build. Even her arms were naturally muscular. Females don't usually have natural upper body strength. Harriett was the exception to the rule. Her beauty and her long painted fingernails contradicted her strong tomboy appearance. I had never seen such long fingernails before. Harriett was a rare find.

I had been swinging on the oak tree at the sand hill with my cousin, Richard. He was older than me and closer to Harriett's age. I was glad I was with him that day, because when we left the sand hill and moved past the grape arbor we walked by Harriett's house. I knew if we saw Harriett, Richard would stop and talk to her and I would be able to stare at her. I had already had my first kiss and she was an older woman of thirteen. I suppose in the back of my newly sexually aroused mind I actually thought there was a possibility I had a shot at Harriett puckering up and planting a big wet juicy one on me. It was my first peek into the world of sexual fantasies. Thank you, Harriett.

As Richard and I approached her house, there she was sitting at a table on her small front porch. My heart went crazy. You remember such moments in your life. I'm sure I had a small case of hyperventilation, but I was sure Richard didn't notice or care as he moved closer to the steps of the porch. At first in my state of "Harriett tunnel vision", I did not see she had a visitor sitting in a chair across the table from her. My heart was still racing from the sight of Harriett, but the blood-pumping cadence changed to a new speed when I realized Billy Wells was sitting on that porch. He was older than Harriett, but the Mayport beauty was socially, mentally, physically and emotionally his equal and probably his superior. I was a substantial number of steps behind my cousin as he reached the steps of the porch. Harriett was cutting something with a large pair of sewing sheers. I could not see what she was cutting.

When Richard reached the bottom step, Billy stood up from the chair and walked to the top of the three steps. My heart raced even faster when I heard his voice.

"Harriett ain't takin' no visitors today, boys. She'll see y'all later."

Well, needless to say, at that moment my feet and pounding heart were both more than ready to turn around and head in any direction other than Harriett's porch. I knew Richard would be turning with me and we would be leaving the premises as Billy Wells had so graciously suggested. No fantasy was worth the possibility of making Billy Wells mad. I had seen the results of his anger. To this day I get a little nervous when I see a red Coca-Cola machine. I was making my exit turn when Harriett's captivating voice stopped me in my fearful tracks.

"Shut up, Billy! Stop bein' so mean to everybody. Hey, Richard."

Harriett stood up and walk next to Billy at the top of the steps. I couldn't believe she told Billy Wells to "shut up". What a woman. She was his equal and I loved her. Her greeting to Richard stopped our retreat for the moment, but Billy Wells made it known he felt he was still in charge. He looked at Harriett, but he talked to Richard.

"You boys go on, now. Go catch some fiddlers or somethin'."

Harriett was in charge of her porch. "Billy, stop it!"

I loved her defiance, but I knew we were not going to make the mistake of staying and visiting, no matter how inviting Harriett looked or her voice sounded. Her brief moment of defiance had given me a little more time to look at her. I was happy with that small moment. Then an incredible thing happened. Harriett looked past my cousin and directed a question to me.

"How's your mama doin', George?" I could not believe she was asking me about my mother. My throat went dry as she continued. "Your mama's so nice to me. I'm workin' with her at Strickland's. She helps me so much. I love Miss Carolyn."

I was Jell-o. I was Silly Putty. She loved my mama. She knew my name. I loved her. I was a pitiful little boy with nothing to do but grin like an idiot. I guess Billy did not like the pleasant chit-chat or my Cheshire cat grin, or the fact in some way we had all defied him. The defiance was not intentional on my part. It was imperative for him to establish his control and dominance over the three of us. Billy Wells put his arm around Harriett's waist and pulled her close to his side.

"She's a pretty thing, ain't she boys?"

"Stop it!" Harriett tried to push him away, but he held her. "I said, stop it!"

At her second, "stop it" I had a fantasy of me running up the steps and making Billy Wells "stop it". My heroic mental moment was short lived when Billy put his big strong hand behind Harriett's head. He pulled her to him and kissed her on her lips. Harriett pushed him with her muscular arms. Billy laughed as he fell backward into one of the chairs. He pulled Harriett down in the chair and onto his lap. The kiss was over, but he still held her. Harriett tried to free herself and they struggled for a few seconds.

Her back was to Billy's chest and he had his arms wrapped around her body. Both his big hands cupped and held Harriett's round and firm breasts. Each time Harriett would force one of his hands away the other would grab at her breasts again.

I don't remember what Richard was doing. I think he was doing the same as me, just watching. I really wanted to help her and I'm sure Richard did, too, but we were both just too scared. I had seen how hard Billy Wells could hit. I'm sad to say I was also excited as I watched him touching her in that way. I kept watching his hands move over her body. I didn't like myself at that moment.

Then it happened. Harriett won my young heart forever. She reached over to the table and grabbed the large pair of scissors. She held them like she was holding a butcher knife. My heart seemed to explode in my chest when the beautiful and sexy Harriett raised the scissors and stabbed Billy Wells in his muscular forearm, causing him to release his strong hold on her. Billy gave out a moan of agony and I recognized his painful grimace from the time he cut his foot at the Mayport School house. People usually make the same distorted face when they feel pain.

Harriett ran off of the porch, past Richard and stopped behind me, as if she was hiding from her, soon to be crazy with anger, victim. Once again, I was frozen with fear for all of us, especially Harriett. We all watched Billy Well as he continued to make his painful faces and he held the top of the scissors in his hand. He was too scared or in too much pain to pull the sharp metal out of his arm. Billy glared at Harriett with fire in his eyes and a blood-red face.

"God dammit, Harriett, you didn't have to do that!"

Harriett did not respond. She stayed behind me, as if I would protect her if Billy decided to come after her. She even touched me one time on my back with her hand. I even think her breasts touched my back as we stood there, but that was just probably wishful thinking on my part. To add to her physical beauty and long fingernails, she smelled great, another first for me. If she needed me I'm sure I would have ran with her if Billy left the porch and headed in our direction. In fact, I'm sure I would have led the way for her to follow. I was surprised when Billy sat down in one of the chairs. It was obvious he was in terrible pain. He looked at Harriett again.

"I can't pull it out. I can feel it in the bone. Dammit, Harriett"

All the mad red blood had left his face as if it was drained away. Billy looked pale. He looked sick. He looked afraid. He was probably in mild shock, but he still looked mean. Why was I the one who witnessed two of Billy's painful moments? Harriett spoke for the first time since she had stabbed him.

"I'll go get my daddy!"

Billy Wells did not like that idea at all. "No! One of y'all help me. Don't tell ya daddy. I was just playin' and I got carried away. Come on, now, don't tell ya daddy. Just help me get it out."

Well, there were three of us. I knew there was no way on Earth I was going up to that porch. I also knew it would be stupid if Harriett even considered standing near him in his present state of pain and anger. Richard was the closest. Billy stepped off of the porch and sat down on the top step, holding his arm with the scissors still embedded in his skin, muscle and bone.

Now, I have to admit, my cousin was the perfect candidate to assist Billy with his painful dilemma. Richard had his own mean streak. He was known to revel in someone else's pain and discomfort from time-to-time. Richard had killed his share of animals and burned hundreds of insects with the heat of the sun and a thick magnifying glass. He was somewhat well known in Mayport for his emotionless ability to bite the head off of a live lizard. Richard became so good at it that his lizard head biting talent was demonstrated periodically as the opportunity presented itself. I'm sure the lizard population in Mayport declined significantly during Richard's chomping stage. I really wasn't surprised when Richard stepped toward Billy. Billy held up his bloody arm.

"When you pull it, do it quick and straight up. When I say 'go' I'll hold my arm down and you pull."

Richard did not hesitate. He took the handle of the scissors in his hand. Billy grimaced in pain again, but Richard held on. Billy coordinated the pull and gave the count.

"On three!" Billy took a deep and painful breath. "One…two…three!"

Billy Wells yelled in pain as Richard pulled the scissors out of his forearm. Billy stood up. Richard continued to hold the bloody scissors as Billy moaned, breathed heavily and blew short bursts of air from his mouth. Billy covered the open puncture wound with his other hand to stop the flow of blood.

Richard stepped back from the steps. He still held Harriett's weapon of choice or should I say, necessity. I knew Richard wanted to keep the cutting tool as a souvenir of that joyful moment. Billy did not thank Richard for his first-aid assistance. He looked past me to Harriett.

"You got a wet rag I can hold against it so I don't bleed to death?"

Harriett was no fool. "I ain't comin' up there, Billy. Go on in the house and find somethin'. There's some rags in the kitchen. Just don't take a new one. You'll know the old ones."

Richard's voice surprised me. "Sit down, Billy. I'll get ya somethin'." Richard walked past Billy and went into the house. Billy sat back down on the steps. He still looked at Harriett.

"You really didn't have to stab me."

Harriett swallowed and took a deep breath. I could tell she was afraid. "You just had to keep showin' off. You caused all that to happen. I don't feel sorry at all."

I did not expect Billy's next commit. "Don't tell ya daddy, Harriett. I really like ya daddy. I don't want him mad at me. I didn't mean to do nothin' bad to ya. I just wanted to come over and see ya." I was sharing a moment of weakness from Billy Wells or perhaps a ploy so he would not get in trouble over his molestation of the beautiful Harriett.

Richard interrupted Billy Wells' moment of regret when he opened the screen door and walked back out onto the porch. "Here's a wet wash rag. Hold it on there tight."

Billy nodded, but still did not thank Richard for the help or the wet rag. Billy stood up and walked toward us. Harriett put her hands around my waist and pulled me against the front of her body as he came closer. She pulled me to the side, off the walkway and into the yard, keeping me between her and Billy. We were about ten feet away from him as he stopped on the walkway near us. He continued to look at Harriett

"You ain't gonna tell, are ya?"

Harriett shook her head. "I ain't gonna tell, if it's over."

Billy nodded. "It's over." When Billy's eyes moved from Harriett to me, I'm sure he could hear my heart pounding in my bony little chicken chest. The meanness had returned, if it had ever left at all. "You ain't gonna tell, are ya little George?"

My throat went dry and I really thought I was going to throw up. I actually felt the small amount of blood that was left in my face drain away to parts unknown. I had no words. I never liked it, but I had been that scared before. I wanted to respond without my voice quivering. Harriett's hands still held my waist. Then it came to me. I knew what to say.

"I don't tell on nobody."

Billy Wells nodded and turned to Richard. "He says he don't tell on nobody, you think he's lyin'?"

Richard shook his head. "No, he ain't lyin'. Nobody'll hear it from us."

Harriett had Richard and I sit with her on the porch for an hour or so, just in case Billy changed his mind about it all being over. I fantasized the entire time we were on the porch with her. Harriett and Richard did most of the talking.

Later Richard hinted that he had kissed Harriett at one of Judy Canova's parties, during a "slap, kiss and hug" game. I never had the honor or privilege to press lips with my ultimate dream girl. Our age difference and maturity level seemed to put me at an insurmountable disadvantage. Even though I saw Harriett laughing and playing around with Billy a day or so after the stabbing incident, I will always remember Harriett standing up to Billy Wells. I didn't want to think she had ever given in to his advances, but in my heart I know she probably did.

PANTY RAIDS

Aunt Carmie raised Cousin Jack. He was a tall, skinny man with deep dark tanned skin. Jack was different from most folks. He was mentally challenged, but his condition was given other names during that particular time. He was one of the Mayport walkers. Jack became known for walking the streets of Mayport at all hours of the day or night. His appearance during the nighttime hours would be startling and scary to the unsuspecting woman or child who might cross his path. He was relatively harmless, but if you did not know Jack, it was very unsettling if he appeared from the dark and quickly walked past you.

Jack became an infamous character in the history of Mayport. It seems that Jack took a fancy to women's underwear. He started stealing lady's panties off the Mayport clotheslines. At first the ladies blamed two young black women, who lived in an old shack near one of the docks. The young women were threatened and then their shack mysteriously caught fire and burned. They left Mayport, but the panties continued to be lifted from the clotheslines. For some strange reason, the panty thief stopped his raids for about two months. The wet panties had time to dry in the wind and sunlight. All seemed to be back to normal.

Then one day, a Mayport woman hung a pair of pink silk panties on her clothesline. Now, at that particular time, most folks in Mayport had only seen the white cotton brand of ladies underwear. Jack was no exception to the "I've only seen the white cotton ones", dilemma. One can only imagine what Jack thought the first time he saw those pink ones and how they must have preyed on his limited mind. No doubt the sight was too much for him to ignore. His retirement from panty lifting was over and he was back on the clothesline circuit.

Some say the woman strategically pinned that pink pair on the clothesline to tempt and entice Jack. It could have been a coincidence that she saw Jack when he made his run at the pink panties and pulled them from the line, sending the two spring action clothespins popping into the air.

The story goes that she chased Jack through the streets of Mayport yelling at him and waving a kitchen butcher knife in the air. During the high pursuit, Jack actually put the pair panties on his head and wore them like a hat as he ran. Jack ran to his house, followed by a group of Mayport women who had joined the chase. He ran up onto the front porch of his house and pulled the door open, disappearing into the front room of the house. Aunt Carmie saw Jack run to his room and heard the commotion on the front porch. She met the female lynch mob at the front door. When the excited women calmed down and explained what had happened, Aunt Carmie went to Jack's bedroom, where he was hiding.

She opened the door to the room and she knew instantly that the women told the truth about her strange nephew. Jack was still wearing his pink panty party hat on his head. A search of his room uncovered over a hundred pairs of white cotton ladies panties in a variety of sizes.

The Mayport tragedy involving Jack took place one night when Jack was making one of his nighttime walks and his good friend ran over him with a car. Jack died on a Mayport street near Strickland's Restaurant and the ferry. Mayport had lost one of its "walkers".

SWING DOWN AT THE SAND HILL.

MR. LEEK'S FISH HOUSE

I THOUGHT YOU WAS OUT SHRIMPIN'

Mr. Tom and Miss Lulu were both big individuals. They raised three sons. The eldest boy was a normal size young man, but the two younger boys were both mammoth individuals. Ray, the middle boy was the bigger of the two. Before his untimely death he tipped the scales at well over an unhealthy five hundred pounds. Buck, the youngest, wasn't far behind his brother at the four hundred pound mark. The Mayport stories ran wild about the eating habits of the family, especially the two boys. Some folks said there would be actual knock down, drag out, fights at the dinner table between the two obese siblings. They fought over the last biscuit, the last fried shrimp and the last fried chicken leg.

There was one story told when the father, Tom, announcing that after dinner they would all go to Jacksonville Beach for a Dairy Queen ice cream cone dessert. After the two boys had eaten every thing on the dinner table, they both went outside and stuck their fingers down their throats so they could throw up and have room for the Dairy Queen treat.

Ray was a kind young man. He would give you the huge shirt off his huge back. Everybody loved Ray. One day he fell as he was stepping out of a trailer. As he stumbled his legs could not support his five hundred pound frame. Both legs broke at the knees and Ray was hospitalized. It was the perfect time for Ray to lose some of his unhealthy weight. While staying in the hospital, he actually gained weight because his family members would sneak double cheeseburgers, candy bars and family size bags of potato chips into the room. It wasn't long after his stay in the hospital that Ray died. Within the next year his mother Miss Lulu died also, leaving the father, the oldest son and the youngest, Buck.

The story has been told that one evening the father was relaxing in his favorite rocking chair. His son Buck walked into the dimly lit room. Tom looked up at his huge son and had a typical Mayport question.

"I thought you was out shrimpin' boy. What ya doin' home?"

Buck was holding an ax at his side. He lifted it up into the air and hit his father in the head, killing him as he sat in the rocker. Folks said Buck really loved his father, but the awful tragedy was due to Buck's addiction to crack cocaine. Another violent and untimely death became part of the history of Mayport, Florida U.S.A.

RACE OF DEATH

Another tragedy with the Wells' name involved took place on a December afternoon when Billy and his father, William Wells Sr., were actually drag racing in separate cars on Mayport Road. The story was told that when William Sr. tried to pass Billy's car, he lost control of his car and drove onto the shoulder of the road. The out of control car ran over two young boys, the Modesky brothers, killing one instantly. The other brother died four hours later at the hospital. It was said that one of the boys was actually beheaded when the front of the car struck them. That could have been an exaggeration that seemed to run rampant when such awful things happen. It was also said that William Wells Sr. changed cars with his son, Billy, before the police arrived. He took the blame for his son's reckless and careless actions. William Wells Sr. had been driving for twenty years but had never gotten a driver's license.

One newspaper article from the Florida Times-Union read: Mayport Man Held: Car Strikes Young Brothers; Both Die.

One boy was killed instantly and his brother was injured fatally yesterday afternoon when a car struck them as they walked along the shoulder of Mayport Road. A third child narrowly escaped injury.

Before the second child died about four hours later at the Baptist memorial Hospital, his father was sped to his side by helicopter from the Mayport Naval Station. The copter landed on the hospital lawn.

The driver of the death car was identified as William Edward Wells.

The accident occurred about 1:30 p.m near Wonderwood Road south of the village of Mayport.

Witnesses said Wells had attempted to pass a second car on the left side, saw heavy oncoming traffic and swung behind the second car to try and pass on the shoulder. The three children loomed ahead.

The third child, Paul Burnett, 9, leaped to safety at the last moment but the two brothers were hit by the front of the car. The vehicle then turned over in the ditch. The cars were traveling at high speed at the time.

Wells told the police he had been driving for 20 years but had never obtained a driver's license.

The driver of the second car was identified as Fabian Bothwell who also gave his version of the accident.

There were three passengers in Bothwell's car. One of them was William E. Wells Jr. The son of the driver of the death car.

Florida Times-Union article read: Man Gets 15 Years in Death of Two Boys

The Mayport shrimp boat captain whose speeding car struck and killed two 7-year-old brothers last Dec. 9 was sentenced yesterday to 15 years in the state prison.

William Wells Sr. was convicted of manslaughter and sentenced to fifteen years in prison. He would serve seven of those years. Is there a possibility that "bad blood" is more than a concept and actually does exist?

BILL
THE THIRD VICTIM
OF THE MAYPORT MURDERS

On the third day after Irene and John's deaths, her father, Bill, stopped by the trailer to see if his daughter and son were there. Billy Wells said, "When he saw his daughter's body on the floor he grabbed a knife from the kitchen and chased me to the back of the trailer." Billy shot his father-in-law in his son's bedroom and then covered the body with dirty clothes. He then sealed the room up with duct-tape.

MAYPORT ROAD HOUSE

When I was fourteen-years-old we had been living out on Mayport Road in a Jim Walter Home on a piece of land, my mother owned. The small section a property had been left to my mother by her grandmother. The same Gramma Aggie I almost had to pucker up and kiss about eight years earlier.

We had been living there for about a year. I was now old enough to venture away from the house and our side of the Mayport Road. Until that time, I had been somewhat limited in my activities. I only wandered as far as the houses of our relatives, who lived about two hundred yards away in the woods and on our side of the road. The relatives were members of my mother's family and they had acquired property after Gramma Aggie's death, too; much more than my mother.

I had been watching a group of young boys playing together in a yard across the road from time-to-time. It was not just two or three boys, but seven or eight and even more at times. I knew my mother was friends with the lady who lived in the house across the road, but I had not gone with her when she visited the lady. I'm not sure why, when or how I crossed Mayport Road, but the day came for me to meet the Cason and Horn boys, a meeting that would desperately change my life.

Sam was the oldest one of the Cason boys. He was nineteen-years-old, short, stocky and hard as a rock. It was easy to see he had that Mayport meanness inside. I remember one time Sam took his brother Jimmy and I to the movie theater in Jacksonville Beach to see a vampire movie at midnight. Sam wore a powder blue silk, cowboy style shirt with pearl colored buttons. A young male usher approached Sam because he had his feet on the back of the seat in front of him. The young man was probably about the same age as Sam. The usher shined his flashlight in Sam's face.

"Please take your feet down off the seat, sir."

I don't think the actual full word "sir" got out of his mouth before a crushing right fist blasted him in the face. It was the same type of blow I had already seen from Billy Wells when I stood frozen in fear at the Coca-Cola machine in the lobby of the Mayport schoolhouse. It was a flash of lightning with no warning, mercy, fear or regret, behind it. I was sitting down that time, yet I was frozen in fear once again. My throat went dry with the anticipation of what would happen next. My heart raced as the usher disappeared into the darkness. I guess he fell to the floor. The only thing I saw was the light of the flashlight rolling away down the incline theatre walkway between the rows of seats. Jimmy was sitting next to me and it was obvious he had witnessed Sam's aggressive nature many times before. I knew once again I wanted to be able to hit that fast and that hard.

My heart pounded harder when I saw the usher rise up from the floor and stand over Sam, who was still sitting in his seat. The young man's nose was dripping with blood as he tried to gather his senses. I couldn't believe my ears as he spoke through the dripping blood.

"I'm sorry." I don't remember the other words of the needless apology. I do remember the drops of blood that dripped onto Sam's new, blue, cowboy shirt. When Sam saw the blood on his new blue shirt he threw his second clinched fist. The connection was even harder than the first. The usher dropped out of sight again. I was amazed when Sam calmly stood up and motioned for Jimmy and I to leave with him. We walked out of the building and walked across the street to the pool hall like nothing happened. I had witnessed two more "sucker punches". It was just another violent moment, Mayport style.

Jimmy was the next Cason brother, age wise. He was sixteen, two years older than me, yet he seemed much older. Jimmy would end up being my best friend during that time, or at least I considered him my best friend. I never really thought Jimmy had any best friends. I don't think he thought along those lines. I would spend more time with Jimmy than anyone else. He was the toughest of all the boys living on that part of Mayport Road. Being with Jimmy did not make me a better person, but it did make me a stronger man.

Jimmy Cason was ready to fight at the blink of an eye and that is about how fast his fist flew when the melee began. It was like he had something in his nature that had to be released from time-to-time.

During my time with Jimmy, we lifted weights, jumped on a trampoline, played tackle football, hunted in the woods with bows and arrows and BB guns. We built forts and dug holes to use during our hard, prickly, green pinecone wars. We hunted for rattlesnakes with machetes and used Cherry Bombs and M-80s to kill chickens and whatever got in the way. One of our forts caught on fire one time while Sam was trying to cook something. Sam made us all pee on the fire, but we could not stop the flames from spreading. A large area of the woods was destroyed.

Jimmy shot and killed a huge German Shepard that was barking and running at us. He slowly and calmly drew back the string of his 30 pound hunting bow and let the steel tipped arrow go, driving it deep into the dog's chest. The canine was only about five feet away from us when Jimmy released the arrow. The big dog was dead in a matter of seconds.

The Cason boys all favored their father, Mr. Earl. When you saw the Cason boys you knew they were brothers. Mr. Earl ruled with an iron hand and a razor strap that hung from a metal hook next to the door on the back porch. I always left and went home when I knew one of the boys was going to take a beating. I wanted to be tough like the others, but I knew in my heart would never be that tough.

Claude was the third brother. He was closer to my age, but Claude was different. He became frustrated easily and at first I did not understand his outbursts and temper tantrums. After a short while and our friendship grew, Jimmy told me Claude was different because he had suffered with Scarlet Fever when he was younger and the illness did something to his brain, causing him to be different.

David was the fourth Cason boy. He was very small and skinny, but it wasn't a weak skinny. He looked hard as a cable with little rock hard muscles in his arms and legs. They called David "Dink". I guess because of his size. Dink was always smiling and laughing. He seemed to be too nervous to be so young. He had a kindness about him that seemed out of place. All the Cason boys were as hard as the jetty rocks in Mayport. You had to become a man to play with the Cason boys.

The Cason boys had a sister. She was the youngest. Her name was Molly Jean. What a great southern name. When members of the family called for her, they would say her name quickly and it would only come out, Mo-Jean. She had the same facial features as all the boys. Being with her brothers on a daily basis made her as tough and rough as a little sister could ever get. Mo-Jean was just like the boys, her body was hard as a jetty rock, too.

The other boys who played with the Cason boys were the three Horn brothers, Bow, Willie and Ben. They called Ben, Dukes. There were other Horn children, but the three boys were the one's I saw most of the time. They were as tough as they come and fit in perfectly with the rough and tumble atmosphere surrounding the Cason boys. Once you added my brother Joe, one more boy named Terry, we called him, Butch, and my cousin Richard to the group, you had a small army of eleven young teen age boys ready for what ever adventure unfolded on Mayport Road.

Mr. Earl was a gill net fisherman and made his living on the shore and in the water of the Atlantic Ocean. The Cason boys worked with their father whenever he needed them. Pulling the gill nets full of fish up onto the beach in the early mornings was hard work. They were up and gone before the sun came up. It created hard people. The boys spent more time pulling in the gill nets than going to school. I could see how hard it was on them all. They didn't seem to mind. It was a way of life for them. I felt bad and wanted things to be better for my friends.

Sam was older and was only with us once in a while. He had other friends and interests. He could drive a car and had a motorcycle at his fingertips. Jimmy had a Mo-Ped he had pieced together. Both Jimmy and Sam were wild and reckless when riding on their motor machines.

Sam and Jimmy had an awful accident while riding on Sam's motorcycle near the Dairy Queen. They were both thrown onto the asphalt road. Jimmy's face hit the concrete curb and most of his front teeth were broken or knocked out. Both young men suffered broken ribs, cuts and bruises. They were both in bed for a week or so. When they recovered, Sam and Jimmy continued their fearless and reckless driving habits.

YOU GOTTA STAY HOME

It is interesting how one's destiny or fate will raise up its head and tell you to heed certain signs and happenings. Many people talk about a person dying at the appropriate time. The usual comment is, "It just wasn't their time." I became a believer in such sayings when I was fifteen years old.

I was excited when I heard the noise of Jimmy Cason's motorcycle as it rolled into our front yard. It was music to my ears. I knew that anytime I was with Jimmy it would be an adventure. I knew our destination would soon be County Powell's ice cream shop in Mayport, where we would play the pinball machines, listen to the music from the jukebox and best of all see the young female beauties that inhabited the immediate area. You would have been shocked at the number of young pretty girls in such a small town. The Canova sisters, Judy, Jane, Jeannie, Janice and Joan were at the top of any young man's list. Harriet was number one in my book but way out of my reach. Julie and Vickie were among the best to choose, if we were in a position to have our pick. But that was not the case at all. They were more interested in the older young men. The Floyd family had their share of beauties as well, with Diane, Beth, Penny, and Elaina. Mayport was truly an odd place for so many of these outstanding young ladies.

I was also excited because my mother did not have to work at Strickland's Restaurant that day, so I did not have to stay with my brother and sisters. My mother already knew about my plans with Jimmy so when I heard the roar of his motorcycle, all I had to do was yell, "I'm goin' now, mama" and I was off to a Mayport adventure. I was actually already sitting on the backseat of the motorcycle with my feet on the footrest when my mother stepped out of the house and got my attention.

"Wait a minute, Bubba." She called me "Bubba" every now and then. "I just got a call from work and they need me to come in tonight. You'll have to ride with Jimmy another time. I really need to work. You'll have to stay home this time." It was obvious she didn't understand how important this was to me. It was as if she just thought I would understand and say good-bye to Jimmy with a smile. How could one night of tips be more important than my trip to Mayport? I wanted to yell, "No!" I wanted Jimmy to ignore her and turn the throttle so we could speed away. Up to that point in my life I don't think I was ever disrespectful to my mother. I did not want to start then. I don't remember all of my words, but I do recall bringing to her attention the unfairness of her request. I also remember getting off the motorcycle when Jimmy said, "Go ahead. We'll go another time. I'll let Claude ride with me today. Mama says I never take him for a ride. Go on. Do what ya mama says. I'll take Claude this time. We'll go another time."

I'm sad to say, I stomped into the house, Jimmy drove across the road to his house and my mother drove away in our black 1955 Mercury. It was a pitiful excuse for a car. The only good thing about the car was that you could pee thought the hole in the backseat floor board and didn't have to stop the car.

One time the water in the radiator hose froze solid during an odd and extremely cold January. The black rubber hose split open and the ice came out. When the cold weather left and the sun came out the ice melted, my cousin hooked up a new hose and that damn car started right up. I did hate that car.

As I watched that piece of junk car roll out onto Mayport Road, I saw Claude run off the front porch of his house and stand next to Jimmy's motorcycle.

I was about fifty yards away, but Claude's body language revealed his excitement from that distance. Claude threw his leg up and straddled the back seat of the motorcycle as Jimmy walked through the front door and stepped out on to the porch. Jimmy said something to Claude as he approached the motorcycle, but I could not hear what he said. Claude jumped off the back seat and stood on the ground so Jimmy could use his foot to crank up the engine. The Mo-Ped motor sputtered as Claude jumped onto the back seat, wrapping his arms around Jimmy's waist.

Jimmy drove the motorcycle in a small circle in the front yard and then drove out of the back gate of the property. I guess my envy and anger kept me standing there, watching as Jimmy and Claude embarked on the Mayport adventure meant for me. The noise of the idling engine changed to a roar when Jimmy rolled back the hand throttle and the machine actually jumped out onto the broken asphalt and gravel of Mayport Road.

I did not see the actual collision, but I did hear the noise from the impact. A car, traveling south from the Mayport Naval Base hit Jimmy and Claude broadside, sending the motorcycle and the two brothers into the air and crashing through the front windshield of the car. The front fender and grill of the car hit Jimmy and Claude on their left sides, crushing Jimmy's left leg from below his hip to his toes. It was told that Claude's leg was completely severed away from his body at the hip. He was dead at the scene.

I did not witness this, but it was also told that Mr. Earl actually saw the accident from their yard and ran to his two sons. When he arrived at the scene and saw Claude first, he tried to attach Claude's leg back to his hip. Jimmy was taken to the local hospital where the attending physician was preparing to amputate his severely damaged leg. It has also been told that Jimmy's mother, Miss Milly, would not give the doctor permission to amputate the leg. Jimmy recovered for eight months in the hospital. His leg healed, but he does walk with a slight limp. Thank goodness for Miss Milly and her strength at that awful time for her and her family.

When I think about that awful Mayport night, I can't help but consider the role of my fate. I was sitting on the back of that motorcycle only five minutes before the accident. I don't like it when people say this but "It was not my time." It was another tragic night in Mayport's history.

JOHN KING'S HAUNTED HOUSE

During my time as a young boy living in Mayport, I was fortunate to live a few houses behind Mr. John King's Haunted House. I sucked up his ghost stories like a sponge and later in my life I would be the only one who had written down his wonderful tales of the ghosts who walk the halls of his old boarding house.

Mr. King's story about his young and beautiful aunt being pitch-forked to death by her lover as she sat in her favorite green rocking chair is the best of all the stories, especially when that old chair rocks with no one sitting in it.

On the nights that Mr. King would allow visitors to his house to see if any from the after life would make an appearance, he would not only tell his ghost's stories, but he would also tell of the many strange characters who had walked the streets of Mayport. Mr. King would set the ghostly tone with his ability to tell a wonderful story as the many visitors were awaiting the appearance of the little man in red, or the bride washing dishes in her pure white wedding gown.

As I grew older, I visited Mr. King many times with friends and even dates. It was fun to bring a stranger to his house and know I would be welcome at any time. I was extremely proud to be a friend of Mr. John King.

In January of 1977 I went to see Mr. King. He liked a story I had written about old East Mayport called "High-Pitched Hum". We sat down on his front porch and we discussed the book, but also the possibility of us joining forces and creating a new book about the Mayport village with his house and ghosts stories as the main topic and background. I was excited at first when he said he liked my ability to tell a story. He was no doubt the best story teller of his time. Mayport has had no shortage of great storytellers. I was also excited that he would think enough of my ability to allow me to write his stories.

I could see as we talked, Mr. King was also excited about the possibilities of our project together. It was almost like I was a young boy again sitting in his living room as the shadows from the candlelight bounced off of the walls. I was overwhelmed by thoughts of what to do with this new venture. I did not know I was way ahead of the time.

"Mr. King, you are such a great storyteller and your voice is perfect for the effect you want. Why don't we do a tape recording of you telling the stories and I'll write a book to go along with the tape. People can read the book and also hear the real John King tell a few of the stories. I think we can make a lot of money."

He was very excited at my suggestion and added to the mix. "Let's set up an evening for me to tell my stories and you tape-record it. It will be more natural for me that way."

I couldn't believe my ears or his enthusiasm. It was perfect; much more than I expected. We planned to gather the next night with friends and some

Mayport children. He would light candles in the living room and set the atmosphere for his haunted tales. It was too perfect and it was not to be.

Mr. John King had a stroke that very evening. The stroke caused blindness and eventual death within a few days. When I told others from Mayport about my meeting with Mr. King the day of his stroke, some said that perhaps the ghosts living in his house did not want me to get his voice or his stories on tape. Just another untimely death and strange Mayport story.

RICHARD
THE FOURTH VICTIM OF THE
MAYPORT MURDERS

After Billy Wells killed his father–in-law he called Richard. A man he thought was having a love affair with his wife, Irene. Billy invited Richard to come to the trailer and smoke some marijuana and discuss the man's relationship with Irene. It is strange that Richard did agree to meet with Billy, but when he tried to leave, Billy stopped him. When Richard reached into a gym bag he was carrying, Billy shot him, but he did not die at first. Billy had to strangle him with a rope to be sure Richard was dead.

THE GUTTING

Billy Wells and Pete were rivals throughout their childhood. The intense rivalry expanded into an all out war as they grew to be men. They became bitter enemies and faced off many times in confrontational situations. Most of the encounters were verbal, but there were enough physical exchanges to make it obvious someone would be seriously injured if their strained relationship continued on its destructive path.

Billy was always a step ahead of Pete. Billy was the stronger of the two, both verbally and physically. Pete just could not get the best of Billy in any situation. Billy was bigger, stronger, better looking and perhaps even smarter. Pete seemed to always be the one who got embarrassed, physically beaten and out smarted by Billy during and after each confrontation.

Years of Billy's victories added greatly to Pete's hatred for his nemesis. Pete's interest in Billy's younger sister, also contributed to the bitter and ugly feud. Pete always blamed Billy for her indifference to him. In reality, she had no interest in Pete whatsoever. Pete would have never believed that.

The tragedy with Billy and Pete came about one night when Billy was getting the best of Pete in a physical confrontation. During the fight Pete pulled out a huge knife and actually gutted Billy. Pete did not just cut Billy; he cut him like he was gutting a huge Mayport grouper. They say someone in Mayport has a picture of Billy lying on the ground with his intestines falling out of his lower body. It would be typical of a Mayport citizen to be sure and get a snapshot of the horrible scene.

Billy survived and did not press any legal charges against his lifetime enemy. The story was told that Billy said he would take care of Pete in his own way and time. Pete left Mayport the night of "the gutting".

CHAIN GANG JIM

The story was told that Jim spent seven years on a Florida chain gang. After he served his time, he settled in Mayport with his wife. Some how, he bought a wreck of a boat called the MisCue. He took the boat out as a commercial fishing boat, trying to catch Red Snapper, Sea Bass and the varieties of Grouper. Jim was friendly and funny to talk with.

I was working on Al Leek's dock when Jim started docking and unloading his catches there. After about two months, we noticed Jim could not keep a steady crew on his boat. No one stayed and worked more than one trip. Jim had a different crew each time the Miscue left the dock. It was said Jim would drink hard liquor and get crazy and physically aggressive and down right mean when he was the captain of a boat on the high seas. It seemed Jim's lack of fishing experience and small catches caused a high level of frustration he was unable to contend with or contain. His frustration, mixed with alcohol consumption made for a volatile outcome.

The day came while the boat was at the dock when Jim was angry with a new member of his crew. There was a physical confrontation that escalated to the level where Jim beat the other man with a sawed-off shotgun and threw him off the boat and into the St. Johns River. It was high tide and the man's limp body floated between two boats and then under the dock. He was unconscious and floating face up. I jumped into the water so I could keep him from drowning. When I got to the floater I held his head up. He coughed and choked, spitting water and blood out of his mouth. The dock foreman, Skinny, threw a rope to me and I tied the rope around the man's body. Skinny then tied the rope to a wench and pulled the man out of the water.

Jim sat in the small wheelhouse of his boat during the entire rescue. The man had cuts on his face and head and was taken to the hospital. When Mr. Leek approached Jim and asked what happened and why he threw the man into the water. Jim replied, "He just made me mad. If I wanted to kill him I would have throwed him into the deep water. I knew he'd wash up on the shore." A day or so passed before Jim was arrested for the beating he had inflicted on a member of his crew.

THE DOCKS AT MAYPORT, FLORIDA

GET HIM AT THE FERRY SLIP

I was standing on the dock one day with Skinny waiting for one of the boats to dock and unload the shrimp and fish that had been caught overnight. A young black man ran into the fish house and yelled for help. He asked Skinny to hide him. It was obvious he was scared and running from someone.

The young man's name was Wanda. He lived in Mayport and he had recently been arrested for having a gun at the local high school. Before Skinny could respond to Wanda's fearful plea, the noise of a car engine made him run out of the fish house toward the river and onto the main dock area. Two men ran into the fish house through the main double doors. One of the men must have seen Wanda out on the main dock because he yelled, "There he is." and the two men ran out toward the dock. Skinny ran toward the main office. I'm not sure why but I followed the two men out to the dock.

My heart raced in my chest when I saw the two men pointing hand guns and shooting down into the water at Wanda. He had jumped off the dock and into the river. He was using the shrimp boats for cover as the men tried to get a clear shot at him. I was frozen to the wooden slats of the dock. I could not hear the guns discharging and it seemed the bullets were being spit from the barrels of the guns. My eyes focused on one of the guns and I realized it had a silencer attached to the end of the barrel. I had only seen a silencer on guns in the movies. I was scared.

I did not think about it at the time, but the two men with the guns never really paid any attention to me. One of the men saw that Wanda had been able to swim his way to another dock and he was floating away and moving with the north flow of the river. I'll never forget what one of the men said. "We'll get him when he tries to leave the water. He'll probably try to come up at the ferry slip." With his comment, both men turned and ran back into the fish house. It was as if I was not standing there at all.

When they hurried through the fish house they met up with Skinny who was holding a shotgun up and pointed at the two intruders. Skinny made a demand.

"Get off this dock!" Neither man responded to Skinny or broke stride as they hurried past him and moved out of the fish house. I joined Skinny as he walked to the double doors. I was feeling safe because of the shotgun and the fact they had left. When we reached the door I could not believe my eyes. The gun toting gangsters were getting into a white Volkswagen Beetle. A third man was at the wheel of the little car so one of the shooters had to climb into the small back seat, pulling the back rest of the front seat forward so he could squeeze into the back area. It made a sad and frightening situation even more ridiculous. We never called the police. Skinny said it wasn't our business.

I do know that Wanda did escape that day because I saw him months later on the dock. It was not long after seeing Wanda that he was killed during a boating accident. The story went that he was shrimping and fell overboard. The boat came back to Mayport without him.

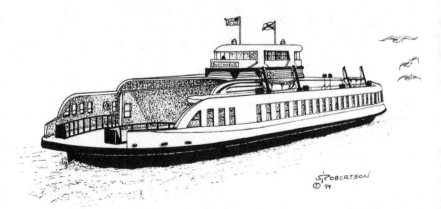

JIMMY
THE FIFTH VICTIM OF THE MAYPORT MURDERS

The last victim of Billy Wells' slaughter was Jimmy, a childhood friend and supposedly a Mayport drug dealer. Billy called Jimmy and asked him to bring crack cocaine to the trailer. Billy said when Jimmy arrived he threatened to take some of his marijuana, so Billy shot and killed Jimmy on the day of his 20th birthday.

Billy said he began smoking the crack cocaine after he had killed his victims in an attempt to stay awake and avoid the suffering he was enduring from his nightmares. Billy said he consumed thousands of dollars worth of drugs during the next week. He even gave some of the drugs away to a number of Mayport drug users so they would help him keep his house clean. Billy cleaned up the evidence of the killings and hid the bodies in the small rooms of the trailer. The visitors ignored the odor of the rotting flesh and other clues of trouble. Billy told police, "So many people came and went, but nobody ever knew. I expected the police to come any day after the first death. I planned to kill myself with that gun."

AFTER THE MURDERS

Billy Wells said his four-year-old son never realized what was happening around him. He kept the boy there with him because Billy expected to die soon. "I wanted to spend my last minutes on Earth with my son." Billy took the boy to school each day and the child returned to spend the night in the trailer surrounded by hidden dead bodies.

The police were called and a neighbor reported Billy Wells had shot their Rottweiler dog. When the officers arrived the owner of the dog would not cooperate with the police and the investigation ended. Billy allowed a friend to enter the trailer, but the visitor had to leave because the odor of the rotting flesh was overwhelming. Another visitor noticed the smell and reported it to the police. The police arrived and Billy threatened to kill himself. The Mayport Murder stand off began. He eventually released his son to the S.W.A.T team and later surrendered, claiming he had overdosed on drugs.

One of Billy's victims was his father-in-law, Bill, the owner of Bill and Angie's Restaurant, located directly across the street from the trailer. It was told that Bill was a former marine with a rather mean streak, of his own, when he got angry.

There was a young man in Mayport named Elton. He was fifteen years old and worked at the restaurant as a bus boy and kitchen help. Now, Elton had grown up on the docks of Mayport and was as tough as a young man could be. One night after the restaurant closed, Bill returned for some reason and found Elton stealing beer from the cooler. Bill shot and killed young Elton. He killed a fifteen-year-old boy.

During the investigation, Bill told the police he did not recognize the boy in the dark and feared for his life. Young Elton's family did not believe the story Bill told. They felt Bill knew it was Elton when he pulled the trigger. After Elton's death, the restaurant had two mysterious fires. An old time Mayport family feud went on for a few years.

A number of years after Bill shot Elton another tragedy occurred. Bill was walking with his two-year-old grandson in front of the restaurant. They were holding hands. The young boy was nearest to the road, not the adult. A truck drove off the ferry boat and passed in front of the restaurant where Bill and the child were walking. The rear tire of the truck hit the child, taking him right out of his grandfather's hand. The child died at the scene. Bill had taken the life of someone's son and now he had lost the life of his grandson. Now, Bill lost his daughter, his son and he died violently at the hands of his son-in-law. There is no doubt there was some "evil goin' on".

EPILOGUE

On my third day as the new principal at Mayport Middle School, a young handsome 8th grader was brought to my office because he was disrespectful to his teachers. The young man had a history of school related problems. I knew when I first saw him he was behind on his grade level and older than the other 8th graders. He sat in the chair in front of my desk, held his head down and did not look at me. I read the improper behavior referral from his teacher and my heart raced when I read his name. He had the same last name as my friend Harriet. I had no doubt he was a relative of the beautiful young woman I knew.

For a moment, I'm ashamed to say, I was not interested in the information in the referral. I was more interested in his relationship to Harriet. One question from me and he lifted his head. We were eye to eye for the first time.

"She's my aunt. My mother's sister."

What are the odds of me running into this young man after all those years? I had no hesitation in asking my next question.

"How is your Aunt Harriet? Does she still live in Mayport?"

Unlike me, he hesitated with his answer, as if he did not want to share any family business; the typical and actually correct southern response to a question from a stranger. I understood. I tried to ease his mind as to my motives.

"I grew up in Mayport with your Aunt Harriet. She was the prettiest girl in town."

He nodded his head, but did not smile. I waited for his response and was not going to continue my personal questions. I looked down at the referral, the actual business at hand and he answered my questions.

"My Aunt Harriet died last week and she was still pretty."

After a guilty plea for the five murders, Billy Wells will spend the rest of his life in prison. His half-brother, the Billy I knew, died of brain cancer a few years ago.

The Mayport Murders is a horrible story of drugs, mental illness, poverty, no concept of the value of human life and pure evil. People make excuses why a person would commit such heinous acts. Some say Billy Wells was a victim of bad surroundings, of drug abuse and poverty. No one will say he may have been destined to kill five people. For years certain members of his family and some friends were connected by meanness, death and pure evil; pure Mayport evil. It may have been a sad matter of Bad Blood.

THANKS FOR
VISITING HISTORIC
MAYPORT
VILLAGE
FOUNDED 1562